£4.10

Printed and Published in Great Britain
by D. C. THOMSON & CO., LTD., 185 Fleet Street,
London EC4A 2HS.
© D. C. THOMSON & CO., 1992.
ISBN 0-85116-531-1

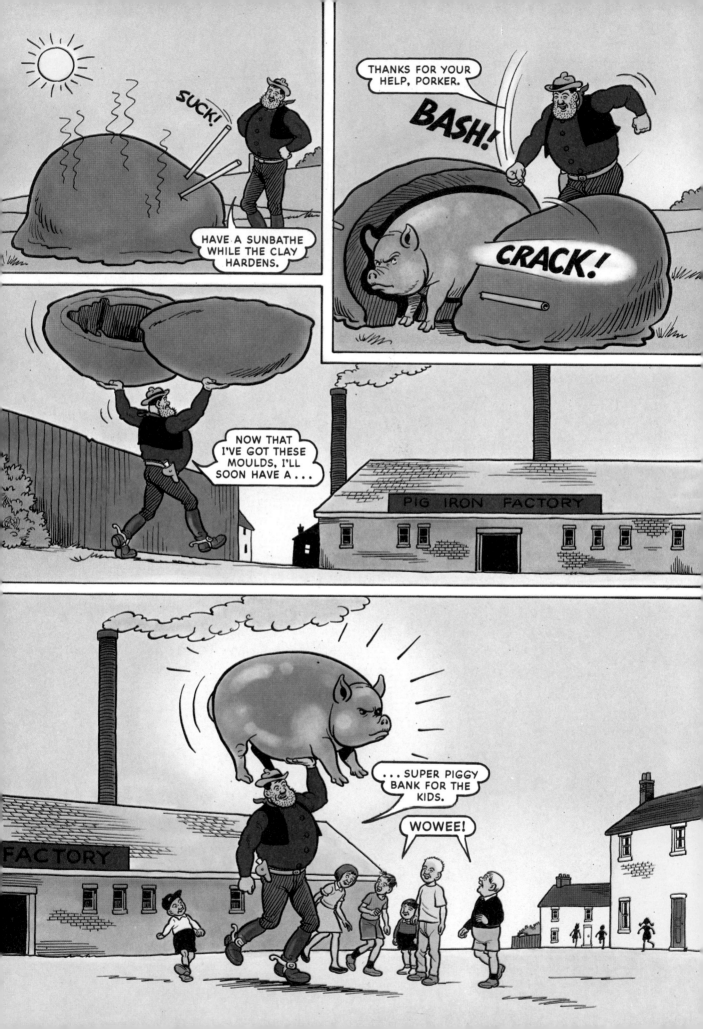

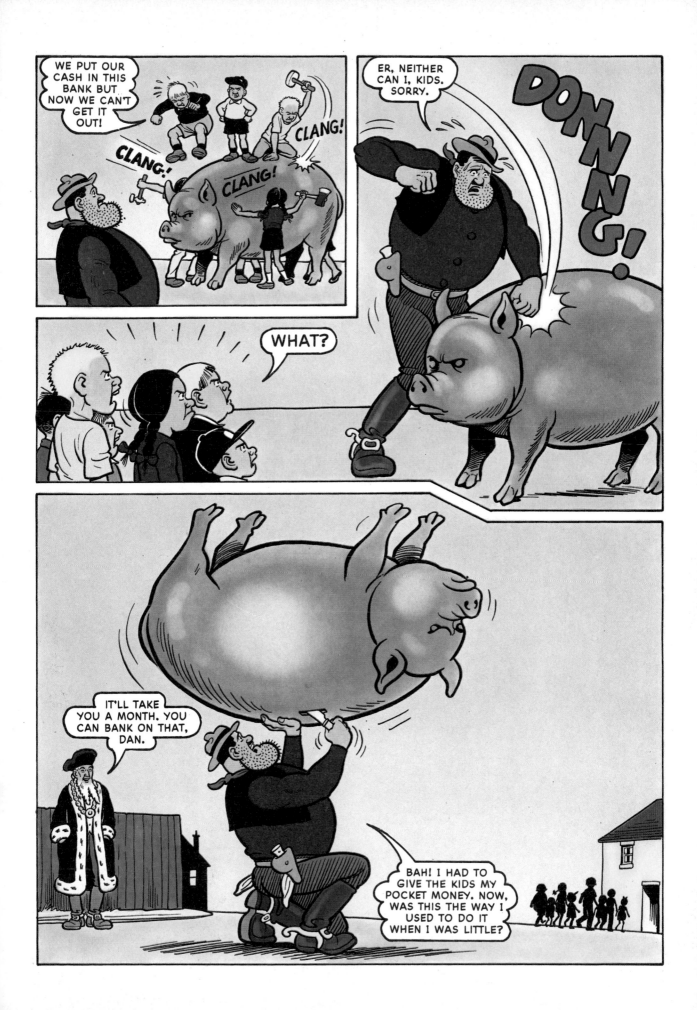

At last —

STUMP UP! I'VE TIED A KNOT!

WHAT? NO CHANCE!

MUM! PETER WON'T PAY ME! WAAGH!

OOPS! TIME TO MAKE A QUICK EXIT, I THINK.

But —

ER — I TIED YOUR LACES FOR YOU, TOO, PETER. NOW I'LL HAVE MY FIFTY PENCE.

CRUMP!

I BOUGHT LIQUORICE LACES. YUM-YUM!

GRR! I'LL TIE YOU IN KNOTS WHEN I GET THESE UNDONE.

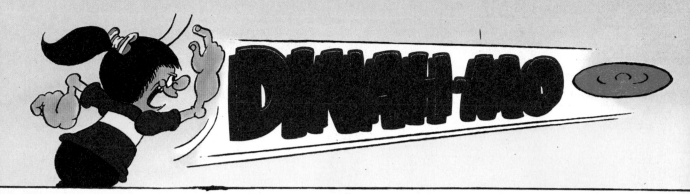

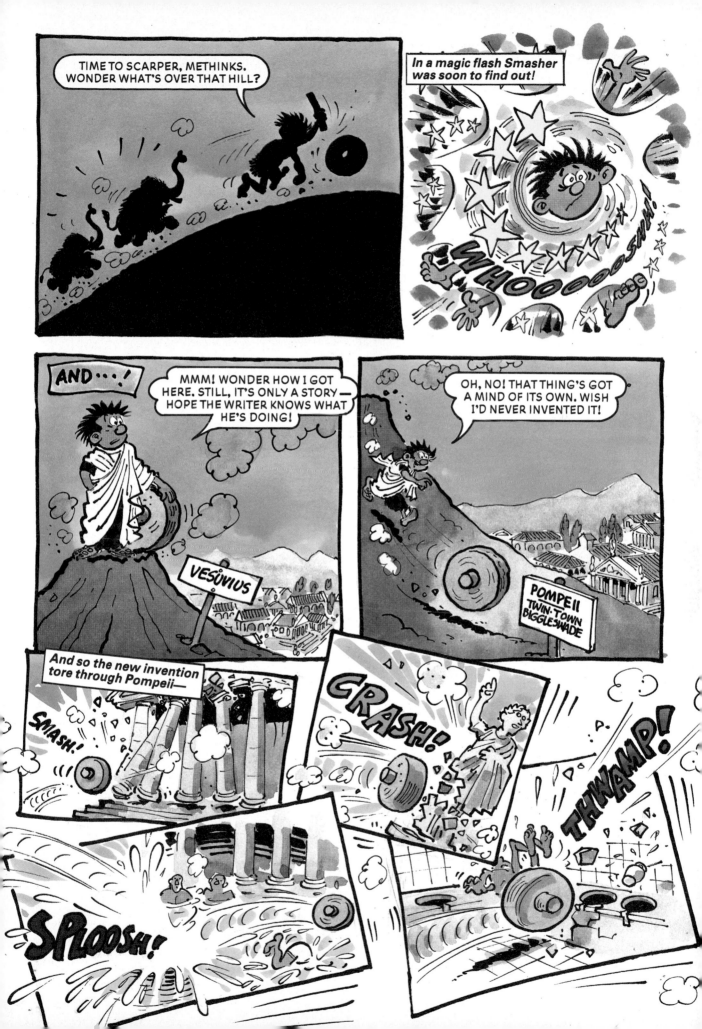

Ralph the Roman

Inside —

Eddie Potter is an ordinary schoolboy.
In fact he's the only ordinary schoolboy
at an extraordinary school for ghouls.

NOBODY'S CHILD

Oh, yeah? Turn to page 113.

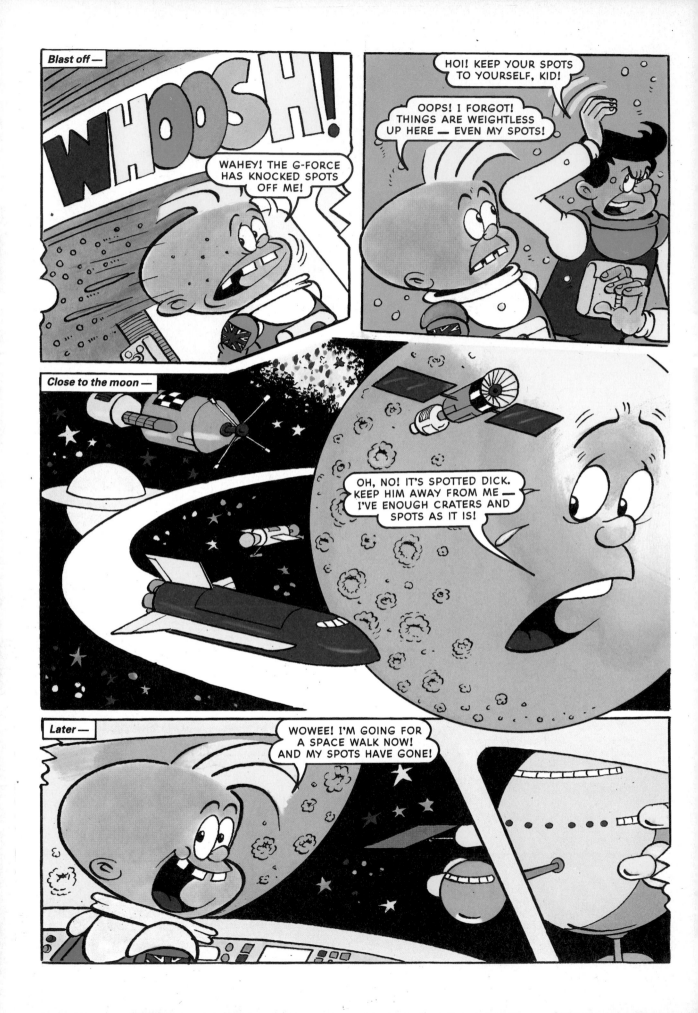

BILLY GREEN AND HIS SISTER JEAN

BANANAMAN

KNIGHT LIFE

Just then—

Next—

But then—

BRASSNECK

G

BILLY GREEN AND HIS SISTER JEAN

H

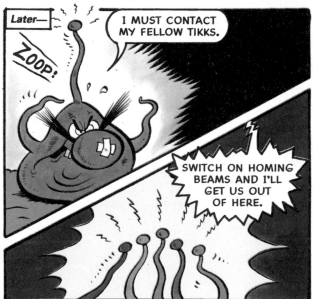